"A quick look at" series

short straight-to-the-point books about emotions, communication & relationship topics, including:

Demystifying Emotions and *Anxiety*

Hypnosis Recordings

Hypnosis can help your subconscious get onboard with your conscious goals.

My *Get Fit and Stay Fit* healthy lifestyle hypnosis helps you get through pangs of desire for foods that aren't on your OK list, whatever that list may be. The general goal is: *"Healthy foods, in healthy amounts, at healthy times of day."* What is *healthy* for you can change throughout an elimination diet experiment and as you put the results into practice as a lifestyle. This hypnosis can support any diet.

My *Release and Refresh* emotional detox hypnosis helps you let go of anything that has burdened, stressed, or overwhelmed you. This hypnosis can help you detox emotionally as you detox physically through your elimination diet and help you flush out any emotions that pop up when you remove eating habits that you have been using to stuff your emotions.

Feed Your Calm

Feed Your Calm: Anti-Anxiety Anti-Stress Diet and Supplement Tips for Stress Resilience explains what's happening to your body under stress, what nutrients help, what foods hurt, and offers a list of foods and supplements to reduce your anxiety. I was writing *Feed Your Calm* when I realized there was a need for a journal to help people through the elimination process so they could test foods to see if they are contributing to their anxiety, so—I created *Discovering How Foods Affect Me: Silver Lining Elimination Diet Journal.*

Journal/Workbooks and Activity Books

Learn, Let Go, Lighten Up: Silver Lining Emotional Detox Journal & Workbook helps you work through anything that burdens or overwhelms you, or gets in the way of you reaching your potential.

Coming soon: other journal/workbooks and emotional intelligence boosting activity books for adults, teens, and children.

Visit annsilvers.com often for the ever-expanding list of self-help products.

DISCOVERING
HOW FOODS
Affect Me

Silver Lining Elimination Diet Journal

Ann Silvers, MA

SILVERSPUBLISHING

ISBN: 978-1-948551-02-1

Printed in the United States of America
8 7 6 5 4 3 2 1

Published by Silvers Publishing, LLC
Gig Harbor, WA, USA
www.silverspublishing.com

Contents

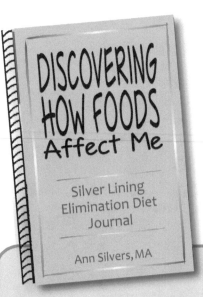

DISCOVERING
HOW FOODS
Affect Me

Silver Lining
Elimination Diet
Journal

Ann Silvers, MA

DIY Journal Add-ons

If you prefer spiral binding for your journals,
you may have a local print shop or copy store that will
convert this journal to a spiral version.

You can also add your own ribbon page-keepers
by taping the ends of a couple of ribbon strips
to the inside back cover.

Preface

I have witnessed how food affects mood over decades of working with counseling clients.

It has been exciting to see a growing appreciation for the impact that food has on not only physical health but also mental health and to become trained in the relatively new discipline of nutritional psychology.

While I was writing *Feed Your Calm*, a book about how foods impact anxiety, I realized that there wasn't an elimination diet journal that I felt I could recommend to readers, so I decided to create one.

I've been through elimination diets myself, some simple targeted elimination experiments and also a very restrictive elimination for SIBO (Small Intestinal Bacteria Overgrowth).

All of my learning—academic, professional, and personal—went into the creation of this journal. Hopefully it helps ease your way through your journey of discovery and helps you get answers to your health puzzles.

-Ann Silvers

The Big 8

While just about any food can cause problems for an individual depending on their biology and situation, eight foods have been identified as being the source of 90% of food allergies.

These foods are known as the Big 8:

1. milk (from cow, goat, and sheep)
2. eggs
3. fish
4. crustacean shellfish (shrimp, crab, lobster . . .)
5. tree nuts (walnut, almond, coconut . . .)
6. peanuts
7. wheat
8. soybean

NOTE: You can be sensitive to (and have problems from) foods that you are not allergic to.

Getting Started

"Those who think they have no time
for healthy eating
will sooner or later have to find time for illness."

-Edward Stanley

Elimination Diet Basics

Congratulations on your decision to take this journey toward a healthier happier you!

An elimination diet helps you identify foods that get in the way of you feeling your best. Exactly what foods are problems for you is very individual (though there are some usual suspects). Eliminating potential culprit foods while you track how you feel mentally and physically can fill in the missing pieces to your health puzzle.

An elimination diet is not a calorie-counting "diet." It is an adventure into discovering how foods affect you.

Different elimination diets

There are many approaches to doing an elimination experiment. This journal is designed to help you through the elimination diet process no matter what approach you are taking.

Here are four basic approaches to doing an elimination experiment, all supported by this journal:

1. **Targeted Elimination:** This is the simplest approach. Eliminate or cut back on one or two foods you think may be a problem.

2. **Observe then Eliminate:** Monitor what you eat and how you feel to see if you can identify any potential problem foods, then do an elimination diet for those foods.

3. **Partial Elimination Diet:** For two to four weeks, eliminate foods that have the highest percentage sensitivity problems for people (gluten and dairy) and some other specific foods that you think might be a problem. Reintroduce foods one by one.

4. **Full Elimination Diet:** Eat a very limited diet for two to four weeks, eliminating the common problem foods and any additional ones that you have identified, then reintroduce foods one by one.

Journal sections

This journal is divided into 4 sections that coincide with different possible phases of an elimination diet:

1. The Observation Phase
2. The Planning Phase
3. The Elimination Phase
4. The Reintroduction Phase

Depending on what type of elimination you are doing, you might use all of the sections, just one, or some combination.

Daily journal pages

Each daily set of journal pages prompts you to track:

- what you take into your body:
    - food (include your beverages other than water)
    - supplements
    - medications
    - water
- other things that might be impacting how you feel:
    - activity (ie work, exercise, going to the beach, . . .)
    - weather

- signs of how you're doing:
    - mood
    - physical symptoms
    - energy (using a numbering system from 1 to 5)
    - sleep
- additional observations or thoughts you want to note

Abbreviations

To make things easier while tracking your life in the next few weeks, you may want to create some abbreviations (abrev's) for things that will appear in your journal repeatedly. You can add to this abrev's list as you go through the diet phases and/or note them on the daily journal pages.

Food	Abrev		Food	Abrev

Supplement Group (ie morning) _____

includes: _____

_____

_____ | Abrev

_____

Supplement Group (ie noon) _____

includes: _____

_____

_____ | Abrev

_____

Medication Group (ie morning) _____

includes: _____

_____

_____ | Abrev

_____

Medication Group (ie noon) _____

includes: _____

_____

_____ | Abrev

_____

Supplement	Abrev

Medication	Abrev

Activity	Abrev		Mood	Abrev
			anxious	
			nervous	
			worried	
			depressed	
			crying	
			sad	
			irritated, irritable	
			angry	
			overly sensitive	
			paranoid	
			jittery	
			on edge	
			calm	
			relaxed	
			happy	
			optimistic	
			excited	

Tracking Energy and Symptom Amount

You can use a 1 to 5 scale for tracking your energy
and also for noting the severity of symptoms.

1 2 3 4 5
lower ....higher
less ....more

Symptom	Abrev		Symptom	Abrev
SKIN			**GI TRACT**	
itchiness			swollen lips	
hives			swollen tongue	
rash			sore throat	
swelling			acid reflux	
redness			excessive saliva	
breakouts			stomach ache	
sores			burping	
			gas	
			bloating	
BRAIN			nausea	
brain fog			diarrhea	
missing words			constipation	
confusion				
mental fatigue				
dizzy				
faint			**PAIN**	
			arthritis	
			sore joints	
RESPIRATORY			general aches	
cough			headache	
shortness of breath			pain in _____	
wheezing				
sinus congestion				
runny nose				
			ATTENTION	
			hyper	
HEART			difficulty focusing	
B.P. change			focused	
chest pain				

About the Notes Section

There is an area on each day's set of pages for you to enter "Notes".

Notes _____

Some things to consider mentioning in the notes section:

- exposure to chemicals, including cleaning products,
- where you are in your menstrual cycle,
- stressors and exceptionally good happenings,
- anything not already noted that could affect your symptoms including energy and mood,
- your thoughts and feelings about how the day is going or went, or about the process in general, and
- anything else you want to note.

Observation Phase

"Curiosity is the fuel
for discovery, inquiry, and learning."

-Terry Heick

USE THIS SECTION IF

you want to monitor what you eat and how you feel to see
if you can identify any potential problem foods, then use
other journal sections to plan for and perform
an elimination diet for those foods.

Day 1 Observation Phase

Date _____

Wake up
Time _____ Energy 1 2 3 4 5
Mood _____

Life is an experiment.
We're always looking for what works and doesn't work.

Time	Food	Sup's/ Meds	Activity	Mood	Symptoms & Energy

Additional Abbreviations Used

My water intake   🥛 🥛 🥛 🥛 🥛 🥛 🥛 🥛

Time	Food	Sup's/ Meds	Activity	Mood	Symptoms & Energy

Notes _____
_____
_____
_____
_____
_____

Time went to bed _____
Sleep quality _____
_____
_____

Date _____

Su Mo Tu We Th Fr Sa

☀ ☁ 🌧 ❄ _____

Wake up
Time _____ **Energy** 1 2 3 4 5
Mood _____

"Always walk through life as if you have something new to learn and you will." -Vernon Howard

Time	Food	Sup's/ Meds	Activity	Mood	Symptoms & Energy

Additional Abbreviations Used

My water intake   🥛 🥛 🥛 🥛 🥛 🥛 🥛 🥛

Time	Food	Sup's/ Meds	Activity	Mood	Symptoms & Energy

Notes _____

_____

_____

_____

_____

_____

Time went to bed _____
Sleep quality _____

_____

_____

Zzzzz...

13

Date _____

Su Mo Tu We Th Fr Sa

Wake up
Time _____ Energy 1 2 3 4 5
Mood _____

"The most useful piece of learning for the uses of life is to unlearn what is untrue." -Antisthenes

Time	Food	Sup's/ Meds	Activity	Mood	Symptoms & Energy

Additional Abbreviations Used

My water intake

Time	Food	Sup's/ Meds	Activity	Mood	Symptoms & Energy

Notes _____
_____
_____
_____
_____
_____

Time went to bed _____
Sleep quality _____

Zzzzz...

_____
_____

Day 4 Observation Phase

Date _____

Wake up
Time _____ Energy 1 2 3 4 5
Mood _____

"The wish for healing has always been half of health."
-Seneca

Time	Food	Sup's/ Meds	Activity	Mood	Symptoms & Energy

Additional Abbreviations Used

My water intake ⎕ ⎕ ⎕ ⎕ ⎕ ⎕ ⎕ ⎕

Time	Food	Sup's/ Meds	Activity	Mood	Symptoms & Energy

Notes _____

_____

_____

_____

_____

_____

Time went to bed _____
Sleep quality _____

_____

_____

Zzzzz...

Date _____

Wake up
Time _____ **Energy** 1 2 3 4 5
Mood _____

"The journey between what you once were and who you are now becoming is where the dance of life really takes place." -Barbara De Angelis

Time	Food	Sup's/ Meds	Activity	Mood	Symptoms & Energy

Additional Abbreviations Used

My water intake 🥛 🥛 🥛 🥛 🥛 🥛 🥛 🥛

Time	Food	Sup's/ Meds	Activity	Mood	Symptoms & Energy

Notes _____
_____
_____
_____
_____
_____

Time went to bed _____
Sleep quality _____

Date _____

Wake up
Time _____ Energy 1 2 3 4 5
Mood _____

"There's nothing like biting off more than you can chew, and then chewing anyway."-Mark Burnett

Time	Food	Sup's/ Meds	Activity	Mood	Symptoms & Energy

Additional Abbreviations Used		

My water intake

Time	Food	Sup's/ Meds	Activity	Mood	Symptoms & Energy

Notes _____
_____
_____
_____
_____
_____

Time went to bed _____
Sleep quality _____
_____
_____

Zzzzz...

Date _____

Su Mo Tu We Th Fr Sa

Wake up
Time _____ **Energy** 1 2 3 4 5
Mood _____

The best way out of a problem is through it.
-Unknown

Time	Food	Sup's/ Meds	Activity	Mood	Symptoms & Energy

Additional Abbreviations Used

My water intake ⊔ ⊔ ⊔ ⊔ ⊔ ⊔ ⊔ ⊔

Time	Food	Sup's/ Meds	Activity	Mood	Symptoms & Energy

Notes _____

_____

_____

_____

_____

_____

Time went to bed _____
Sleep quality _____

_____

_____

Zzzzz...

Day 8 Observation Phase

Date _____

Wake up
Time _____ **Energy** 1 2 3 4 5
Mood _____

You've accomplished a whole week!
Onward & upward to week two.

Time	Food	Sup's/ Meds	Activity	Mood	Symptoms & Energy

Additional Abbreviations Used

24

My water intake

Time	Food	Sup's/ Meds	Activity	Mood	Symptoms & Energy

Notes _____
_____
_____
_____
_____
_____

Time went to bed _____
Sleep quality _____
_____
_____

Zzzzz...

Day 9

Observation Phase

Date _____

Su Mo Tu We Th Fr Sa

☀ ☁ 🌧 ❄ _____

Wake up
Time _____ Energy 1 2 3 4 5
Mood _____

"A healthy attitude is contagious, but don't wait to catch it from others. Be a carrier." -Tom Stoppard

Time	Food	Sup's/ Meds	Activity	Mood	Symptoms & Energy

Additional Abbreviations Used

My water intake

Time	Food	Sup's/ Meds	Activity	Mood	Symptoms & Energy

Notes _____

_____

_____

_____

_____

Time went to bed _____

Sleep quality _____

_____

_____

Date _____

Wake up
Time _____ Energy 1 2 3 4 5
Mood _____

"You have learnt something. That always feels at first as if you had lost something."-George Bernard Shaw

Time	Food	Sup's/ Meds	Activity	Mood	Symptoms & Energy

Additional Abbreviations Used

My water intake ☐ ☐ ☐ ☐ ☐ ☐ ☐ ☐

Time	Food	Sup's/ Meds	Activity	Mood	Symptoms & Energy

Notes _____
_____
_____
_____
_____
_____

Time went to bed _____
Sleep quality _____
_____
_____

Zzzzz...

Day 11 Observation Phase

Date _____

Su Mo Tu We Th Fr Sa

☀ ☁ 🌧 ❄ _____

Wake up
Time _____ Energy 1 2 3 4 5
Mood _____

"Man stands for long time with mouth open before roast duck flies in." -Chinese Proverb (a little food humor to ponder)

Time	Food	Sup's/ Meds	Activity	Mood	Symptoms & Energy

Additional Abbreviations Used

My water intake

Time	Food	Sup's/ Meds	Activity	Mood	Symptoms & Energy

Notes _____

_____

_____

_____

_____

_____

Time went to bed _____
Sleep quality _____

_____

_____

Date _____

Wake up
Time _____ Energy 1 2 3 4 5
Mood _____

"The difference between try and triumph is a little umph."
-Marvin Phillips

Time	Food	Sup's/ Meds	Activity	Mood	Symptoms & Energy

Additional Abbreviations Used

My water intake   🥛 🥛 🥛 🥛 🥛 🥛 🥛 🥛

Time	Food	Sup's/ Meds	Activity	Mood	Symptoms & Energy

Notes _____

_____

_____

_____

_____

Time went to bed _____
Sleep quality _____

Zzzz...

_____

_____

Date _____

Wake up
Time _____ Energy 1 2 3 4 5
Mood _____

"Today is the oldest you have been, and the youngest you will ever be. Make the most of it!" -Nicky Gumbel

Time	Food	Sup's/ Meds	Activity	Mood	Symptoms & Energy

Additional Abbreviations Used

My water intake ☐ ☐ ☐ ☐ ☐ ☐ ☐ ☐

Time	Food	Sup's/ Meds	Activity	Mood	Symptoms & Energy

Notes _____
_____
_____
_____
_____
_____

Time went to bed _____
Sleep quality _____

Zzzzz...

_____
_____

Day 14 Observation Phase

Date _____

Su Mo Tu We Th Fr Sa

 Wake up
Time _____ **Energy** 1 2 3 4 5
Mood _____

You have arrived at your goal! Well done!

Time	Food	Sup's/ Meds	Activity	Mood	Symptoms & Energy

Additional Abbreviations Used

My water intake

Time	Food	Sup's/ Meds	Activity	Mood	Symptoms & Energy

Notes _____

_____

_____

_____

_____

_____

Time went to bed _____

Sleep quality _____

_____

_____

Reflections on Observation Phase

Foods that appear suspect

Symptoms	Suspect Food	Notes

Planning Phase

"Our goals can only be reached through a vehicle
of a plan, in which we must fervently believe,
and upon which we must vigorously act.
There is no other route to success."

-Pablo Picasso

USE THIS SECTION TO

plan for your elimination diet.

Make a Plan

It can be very helpful for you to take time to plan for your elimination diet: think through your start date, figure out what you'll be eating instead of your old go-to's, stock up on the foods that are on your diet, and possibly remove temptation.

Use this page to think through some timing and preparation options and make some decisions. Take a tour of the planning pages to get a feel for what is involved before answering the questions.

Do I want to do a pre-elimination reduction?

You might want to cut back on a food or beverage (like coffee) before you totally eliminate it.

_____

_____

_____

_____

Should I do some practice runs?

You might want to practice recipes, substitutions . . . before your official elimination diet start date.

_____

_____

_____

_____

When to start the elimination phase?

Give yourself some time to prepare. You might want to time the beginning with a weekend to get through the most challenging couple of days. Is there a special event you want to plan around?

_____

_____

_____

_____

To Do List

Some of the items on this list won't apply to you—just put a line through those.

Started / Completed

- [ ] Pick a start date [ ]
- [ ] Foods to Eliminate list [ ]
- [ ] Foods Included in Diet list [ ]
- [ ] Meal ideas [ ]
- [ ] Cupboard cleanse [ ]
- [ ] Grocery list [ ]
- [ ] Get groceries [ ]
- [ ] Pre-elimination reduction [ ]
- [ ] Practice runs [ ]
- [ ] [ ]
- [ ] [ ]
- [ ] [ ]
- [ ] [ ]
- [ ] [ ]
- [ ] [ ]
- [ ] [ ]
- [ ] [ ]
- [ ] [ ]
- [ ] [ ]
- [ ] [ ]
- [ ] [ ]

Foods to Eliminate

For this list, a "food group" could be something like gluten, and "specific foods" gluten sources like wheat, rye, barley, malt . . .

Food Group	Specific Foods	Notes

Foods Included in Diet

If you are doing a targeted elimination, then you might want to use this list for eliminated foods' substitutions. If you are doing a very strict elimination diet, then you may want to list what foods are left as your edibles.

Food Group	Specific Foods	Notes

Meal Ideas

It can be helpful to think about your elimination diet meal and beverage options. You might want to do some internet searches to see what other people have done and gather some recipes.

Breakfast

1.

2.

3.

Beverages

Morning Snack

1.

2.

3.

Beverages

Lunch

1.

2.

3.

4.

5.

Beverages

Afternoon Snack

1.
2.
3.

Beverages

Dinner

1.
2.
3.
4.
5.

Beverages

Restaurant Meals

1.
2.
3.
4.
5.

Beverages

Cupboard Cleanse

It can be helpful to clear your cupboard of temptation before beginning the elimination phase of your journey. You can list what you want to clear out below.

- [ ]
- [ ]
- [ ]
- [ ]
- [ ]
- [ ]
- [ ]
- [ ]
- [ ]
- [ ]
- [ ]
- [ ]
- [ ]
- [ ]
- [ ]
- [ ]
- [ ]
- [ ]
- [ ]
- [ ]

Grocery List

- [ ]
- [ ]
- [ ]
- [ ]
- [ ]
- [ ]
- [ ]
- [ ]
- [ ]
- [ ]
- [ ]
- [ ]
- [ ]
- [ ]
- [ ]
- [ ]
- [ ]
- [ ]
- [ ]
- [ ]
- [ ]
- [ ]
- [ ]

Elimination Tips

The elimination phase helps you clear your body from negative effects of foods that you have been eating in the past.

As you move through this phase, monitor for physical symptoms, energy, mood and the quality of your sleep (ie how difficult it is to get to sleep, and how well and how long you sleep). The journal pages also include prompts for tracking other things that might impact how you are feeling: the weather, activities, supplements and medications.

Even if your included foods list is small, make sure you get enough protein throughout the day.

This phase typically lasts 2 weeks, but may be 3 or 4 weeks depending on how long it takes you to feel better or the particulars of your program. (The journal gives you 4 weeks' worth of tracking pages.)

If you are doing a simple targeted elimination, you might feel so much better during the elimination that you decide to stay off of that food or foods and you don't need the reintroduction phase. You just move on with your life with a changed diet and a healthier happier you.

DETOX WARNING

You may actually feel worse the first week or so on an elimination diet as your body detoxes.

It's important to keep up your water intake to help you flush out the messy buildup from your previous diet.

(Contact a doctor if you experience severe symptoms.)

Elimination Phase

"We don't receive wisdom;
we must discover it for ourselves
after a journey that no one can take for us
or spare us."

-Marcel Proust

USE THIS SECTION FOR

a 2-4 week partial or full elimination diet.

Date _____

Su Mo Tu We Th Fr Sa

Wake up
Time _____ Energy 1 2 3 4 5
Mood _____

"You have set yourselves a difficult task, but you will succeed if you persevere; and you will find a joy in overcoming obstacles." -Helen Keller

Time	Food	Sup's/ Meds	Activity	Mood	Symptoms & Energy

Additional Abbreviations Used

My water intake ⊔ ⊔ ⊔ ⊔ ⊔ ⊔ ⊔ ⊔

Time	Food	Sup's/ Meds	Activity	Mood	Symptoms & Energy

Notes _____
_____
_____
_____
_____
_____

Time went to bed _____
Sleep quality _____
_____
_____

Zzzzz...

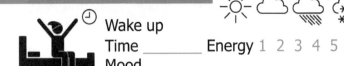

Day 2 Elimination Phase

Date _____

Su Mo Tu We Th Fr Sa

Wake up
Time _____ Energy 1 2 3 4 5
Mood _____

"To get where you want to go you can't only do what you like."
-Peter Abrahams

Time	Food	Sup's/ Meds	Activity	Mood	Symptoms & Energy

Additional Abbreviations Used

My water intake ▯ ▯ ▯ ▯ ▯ ▯ ▯ ▯

Time	Food	Sup's/ Meds	Activity	Mood	Symptoms & Energy

Notes _____
_____
_____
_____
_____
_____

Time went to bed _____
Sleep quality _____
_____
_____

Zzzzz...

Elimination Phase

Date _____

Su Mo Tu We Th Fr Sa

Wake up
Time _____ Energy 1 2 3 4 5
Mood _____

"To get through the hardest journey we need take only one step at a time, but we must keep on stepping." -Chinese Proverb

Time	Food	Sup's/ Meds	Activity	Mood	Symptoms & Energy

Additional Abbreviations Used

My water intake   ☐ ☐ ☐ ☐ ☐ ☐ ☐ ☐

Time	Food	Sup's/ Meds	Activity	Mood	Symptoms & Energy

Notes _____
_____
_____
_____
_____
_____

Time went to bed _____
Sleep quality _____
_____
_____

Zzzzz...

Date _____

Su Mo Tu We Th Fr Sa

Wake up
Time _____ Energy 1 2 3 4 5
Mood _____

*"Some say the glass is half empty, some say the glass is half full,
I say, . . . are you going to drink that?"*-Lisa Claymen

Time	Food	Sup's/ Meds	Activity	Mood	Symptoms & Energy

Additional Abbreviations Used

My water intake

Time	Food	Sup's/ Meds	Activity	Mood	Symptoms & Energy

Notes _____
_____
_____
_____
_____

Time went to bed _____
Sleep quality _____
_____
_____

Day 5 Elimination Phase

Date _____

Su Mo Tu We Th Fr Sa

 _____

Wake up
Time _____ **Energy** 1 2 3 4 5
Mood _____

"All doors are hard to unlock until you have the key."
-Robert C. O'Brien

Time	Food	Sup's/ Meds	Activity	Mood	Symptoms & Energy

Additional Abbreviations Used

My water intake 🥛 🥛 🥛 🥛 🥛 🥛 🥛 🥛

Time	Food	Sup's/ Meds	Activity	Mood	Symptoms & Energy

Notes _____

_____

_____

_____

_____

Time went to bed _____
Sleep quality _____

_____

61

Day 6 Elimination Phase

Wake up
Time _____ Energy 1 2 3 4 5
Mood _____

"Courage is not simply one of the virtues, but the form of every virtue at the testing point."-CS Lewis

Time	Food	Sup's/ Meds	Activity	Mood	Symptoms & Energy

Additional Abbreviations Used

My water intake

Time	Food	Sup's/ Meds	Activity	Mood	Symptoms & Energy

Notes _____

_____

_____

_____

_____

_____

Time went to bed _____
Sleep quality _____

_____

Zzzz...

Day 7 Elimination Phase

Wake up
Time _____ **Energy** 1 2 3 4 5
Mood _____

"Learning is a gift. Even when pain is your teacher."
-Maya Watson

Time	Food	Sup's/ Meds	Activity	Mood	Symptoms & Energy

Additional Abbreviations Used

My water intake ⊔ ⊔ ⊔ ⊔ ⊔ ⊔ ⊔ ⊔

Time	Food	Sup's/ Meds	Activity	Mood	Symptoms & Energy

Notes _____
_____
_____
_____
_____

Time went to bed _____
Sleep quality _____
_____
_____

Zzzzz...

65

Day 8 Elimination Phase

Date _____

Su Mo Tu We Th Fr Sa

Wake up
Time _____ **Energy** 1 2 3 4 5
Mood _____

You've accomplished a whole week! Bravo!

Time	Food	Sup's/ Meds	Activity	Mood	Symptoms & Energy

Additional Abbreviations Used

My water intake

Time	Food	Sup's/ Meds	Activity	Mood	Symptoms & Energy

Notes _____

_____

_____

_____

_____

_____

Time went to bed _____
Sleep quality _____

_____

_____

Date _____

Su Mo Tu We Th Fr Sa

Wake up
Time _____ Energy 1 2 3 4 5
Mood _____

"Commitment leads to action. Action brings your dream closer."
-Marcia Wieder

Time	Food	Sup's/ Meds	Activity	Mood	Symptoms & Energy

Additional Abbreviations Used

My water intake   🥛 🥛 🥛 🥛 🥛 🥛 🥛 🥛

Time	Food	Sup's/ Meds	Activity	Mood	Symptoms & Energy

Notes _____

_____

_____

_____

_____

Time went to bed _____
Sleep quality _____

_____

_____

Day 10 Elimination Phase

Date _____

Wake up
Time _____ Energy 1 2 3 4 5
Mood _____

"Recognize joy when it arrives in the plain brown wrappings of everyday life." -Judith Viorst

Time	Food	Sup's/ Meds	Activity	Mood	Symptoms & Energy

Additional Abbreviations Used

My water intake

Time	Food	Sup's/ Meds	Activity	Mood	Symptoms & Energy

Notes _____
_____
_____
_____
_____

Time went to bed _____
Sleep quality _____
_____
_____

Zzzzz...

Date _____

Su Mo Tu We Th Fr Sa

Wake up
Time _____ Energy 1 2 3 4 5
Mood _____

"We are responsible for what we are, and whatever we wish ourselves to be, we have the power to make ourselves."-Swami Vivekananda

Time	Food	Sup's/ Meds	Activity	Mood	Symptoms & Energy

Additional Abbreviations Used

My water intake ⊔ ⊔ ⊔ ⊔ ⊔ ⊔ ⊔ ⊔

Time	Food	Sup's/ Meds	Activity	Mood	Symptoms & Energy

Notes _____
_____
_____
_____
_____
_____

Time went to bed _____
Sleep quality _____
_____
_____

Zzzzz...

Date _____

Wake up
Time _____ **Energy** 1 2 3 4 5
Mood _____

The best view comes after the hardest climb.

-Unknown

Time	Food	Sup's/ Meds	Activity	Mood	Symptoms & Energy

Additional Abbreviations Used

My water intake 🥛 🥛 🥛 🥛 🥛 🥛 🥛 🥛

Time	Food	Sup's/ Meds	Activity	Mood	Symptoms & Energy

Notes _____

_____

_____

_____

_____

_____

Time went to bed _____
Sleep quality _____

_____

_____

Zzzzz...

Day 13 Elimination Phase

Date _____

Su Mo Tu We Th Fr Sa

Wake up
Time _____ **Energy** 1 2 3 4 5
Mood _____

"In the middle of every difficulty lies opportunity."
-Albert Einstein

Time	Food	Sup's/ Meds	Activity	Mood	Symptoms & Energy

Additional Abbreviations Used

My water intake

Time	Food	Sup's/ Meds	Activity	Mood	Symptoms & Energy

Notes _____

_____

_____

_____

_____

_____

Time went to bed _____
Sleep quality _____

_____

_____

Date _____

Su Mo Tu We Th Fr Sa

Wake up
Time _____ **Energy** 1 2 3 4 5
Mood _____

Today is 2 weeks! Congrats! The last day of elimination or the beginning of the home stretch.

Time	Food	Sup's/ Meds	Activity	Mood	Symptoms & Energy

Additional Abbreviations Used

My water intake　🥛 🥛 🥛 🥛 🥛 🥛 🥛 🥛

Time	Food	Sup's/ Meds	Activity	Mood	Symptoms & Energy

Notes _____

_____

_____

_____

_____

Time went to bed _____
Sleep quality _____

_____

_____

Zzzzz...

Date _____

Su Mo Tu We Th Fr Sa

☀ ☁ 🌧 ❄

Wake up

Time _____ Energy 1 2 3 4 5

Mood _____

"All things are difficult before they are easy."
-Thomas Fuller

Time	Food	Sup's/ Meds	Activity	Mood	Symptoms & Energy

Additional Abbreviations Used

My water intake

Time	Food	Sup's/ Meds	Activity	Mood	Symptoms & Energy

Notes _____

_____

_____

_____

_____

_____

Time went to bed _____
Sleep quality _____

_____

_____

Day 16 Elimination Phase

Date _____

Wake up
Time _____ Energy 1 2 3 4 5
Mood _____

"A man too busy to take care of his health is like a mechanic too busy to take care of his tools."-Spanish proverb

Time	Food	Sup's/ Meds	Activity	Mood	Symptoms & Energy

Additional Abbreviations Used

My water intake   ▯ ▯ ▯ ▯ ▯ ▯ ▯ ▯

Time	Food	Sup's/ Meds	Activity	Mood	Symptoms & Energy

Notes _____
_____
_____
_____
_____
_____

Time went to bed _____
Sleep quality _____
_____
_____

Day 17 Elimination Phase

Date _____

Su Mo Tu We Th Fr Sa

Wake up
Time _____ Energy 1 2 3 4 5
Mood _____

"There's always a moment that separates the past from the future, and that moment is now." -Aniekee Tochukwu Ezekiel

Time	Food	Sup's/ Meds	Activity	Mood	Symptoms & Energy

Additional Abbreviations Used

My water intake

Time	Food	Sup's/ Meds	Activity	Mood	Symptoms & Energy

Notes _____

_____

_____

_____

_____

_____

Time went to bed _____
Sleep quality _____

_____

Zzzzz...

Date _____

Wake up
Time _____ Energy 1 2 3 4 5
Mood _____

"Some people want it to happen, some wish it would happen, others make it happen."-Michael Jordan

Time	Food	Sup's/ Meds	Activity	Mood	Symptoms & Energy

Additional Abbreviations Used

My water intake

Time	Food	Sup's/ Meds	Activity	Mood	Symptoms & Energy

Notes _____

_____

_____

_____

_____

_____

Time went to bed _____
Sleep quality _____

_____

_____

Day 19 Elimination Phase

Date _____

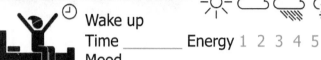

_____

Wake up
Time _____ **Energy** 1 2 3 4 5
Mood _____

I'm going to stand outside. So if anyone asks, I'm outstanding.

-Unknown

Time	Food	Sup's/ Meds	Activity	Mood	Symptoms & Energy

Additional Abbreviations Used

My water intake

Time	Food	Sup's/ Meds	Activity	Mood	Symptoms & Energy

Notes _____
_____
_____
_____
_____
_____

Time went to bed _____
Sleep quality _____
_____

Day 20 Elimination Phase

Date _____

Su Mo Tu We Th Fr Sa

Wake up
Time _____ **Energy** 1 2 3 4 5
Mood _____

*"Never underestimate the power you have
to take your life in a new direction."* -Germany Kent

Time	Food	Sup's/ Meds	Activity	Mood	Symptoms & Energy

Additional Abbreviations Used

My water intake

Time	Food	Sup's/ Meds	Activity	Mood	Symptoms & Energy

Notes _____

_____

_____

_____

_____

_____

Time went to bed _____
Sleep quality _____

Zzzzz...

_____

_____

Date _____

Su Mo Tu We Th Fr Sa

Wake up
Time _____ Energy 1 2 3 4 5
Mood _____

You made it to 3 weeks! Yeah you!

Time	Food	Sup's/ Meds	Activity	Mood	Symptoms & Energy

Additional Abbreviations Used

My water intake ▯ ▯ ▯ ▯ ▯ ▯ ▯ ▯

Time	Food	Sup's/ Meds	Activity	Mood	Symptoms & Energy

Notes _____
_____
_____
_____
_____
_____

Time went to bed _____
Sleep quality _____

Zzzzz...

_____

Day 22 Elimination Phase

Date _____

Wake up
Time _____ Energy 1 2 3 4 5
Mood _____

"Life is not about waiting for the storms to pass. It's about learning how to dance in the rain." -Vivian Greene

Time	Food	Sup's/ Meds	Activity	Mood	Symptoms & Energy

Additional Abbreviations Used

My water intake 🥛 🥛 🥛 🥛 🥛 🥛 🥛 🥛

Time	Food	Sup's/ Meds	Activity	Mood	Symptoms & Energy

Notes _____
_____
_____
_____
_____

Time went to bed _____
Sleep quality _____
_____
_____

Zzzz...

Day 23 Elimination Phase

Wake up
Time _____ **Energy** 1 2 3 4 5
Mood _____

It's never too early or too late to work towards being the healthiest you. -Unknown

Time	Food	Sup's/ Meds	Activity	Mood	Symptoms & Energy

Additional Abbreviations Used

My water intake 🥛 🥛 🥛 🥛 🥛 🥛 🥛 🥛

Time	Food	Sup's/ Meds	Activity	Mood	Symptoms & Energy

Notes _____
_____
_____
_____
_____
_____

Time went to bed _____
Sleep quality _____
_____

Date _____

Wake up
Time _____ Energy 1 2 3 4 5
Mood _____

"People often say that motivation doesn't last. Well, neither does bathing; that's why we recommend it daily."-Zig Ziglar

Time	Food	Sup's/ Meds	Activity	Mood	Symptoms & Energy

Additional Abbreviations Used

My water intake ▢ ▢ ▢ ▢ ▢ ▢ ▢ ▢

Time	Food	Sup's/ Meds	Activity	Mood	Symptoms & Energy

Notes _____
_____
_____
_____
_____
_____

Time went to bed _____
Sleep quality _____
_____
_____

Zzzz...

Date _____

Su Mo Tu We Th Fr Sa

☀ ☁ 🌧 ❄ _____

Wake up

Time _____ **Energy** 1 2 3 4 5

Mood _____

"Just when the caterpillar thought the world was ending,
he turned into a butterfly." -Proverb

Time	Food	Sup's/ Meds	Activity	Mood	Symptoms & Energy

Additional Abbreviations Used

My water intake

Time	Food	Sup's/ Meds	Activity	Mood	Symptoms & Energy

Notes _____

_____

_____

_____

_____

_____

Time went to bed _____
Sleep quality _____

_____

_____

Zzzzz...

Date _____

Su Mo Tu We Th Fr Sa

☀ ☁ ☔ ❄ _____

Wake up
Time _____ **Energy** 1 2 3 4 5
Mood _____

"Take care of your body. It's the only place you have to live in."

-Jim Rohn

Time	Food	Sup's/ Meds	Activity	Mood	Symptoms & Energy

Additional Abbreviations Used

My water intake

Time	Food	Sup's/ Meds	Activity	Mood	Symptoms & Energy

Notes _____

_____

_____

_____

_____

_____

Time went to bed _____
Sleep quality _____

_____

_____

Zzzzz...

Date _____

Su Mo Tu We Th Fr Sa

Wake up
Time _____ Energy 1 2 3 4 5
Mood _____

"Let perseverance be your engine and hope your fuel."
-H. Jackson Brown, Jr.

Time	Food	Sup's/ Meds	Activity	Mood	Symptoms & Energy

Additional Abbreviations Used

My water intake

Time	Food	Sup's/ Meds	Activity	Mood	Symptoms & Energy

Notes _____

_____

_____

_____

_____

Time went to bed _____
Sleep quality _____

_____

_____

Day 28 Elimination Phase

Date _____

Su Mo Tu We Th Fr Sa

Wake up
Time _____ **Energy** 1 2 3 4 5
Mood _____

Ta dah! You made it!

Time	Food	Sup's/ Meds	Activity	Mood	Symptoms & Energy

Additional Abbreviations Used

My water intake ▯ ▯ ▯ ▯ ▯ ▯ ▯ ▯

Time	Food	Sup's/ Meds	Activity	Mood	Symptoms & Energy

Notes _____
_____
_____
_____
_____
_____

Time went to bed _____
Sleep quality _____

Zzzzz...

_____

Reflections on Elimination Phase

Foods that Appear Suspect

Symptoms	Suspect Food	Notes

Reintroduction Phase

"It is good to have an end to journey toward,
but it is the journey that matters in the end."

-Ursula K. Le Guin

USE THIS SECTION IF

you want to reintroduce foods that you previously
eliminated so you can monitor for reactions.

Reintroduction Tips

The reintroduction phase helps you test foods one at a time while you monitor for effects.

This phase has testing cycles that typically last 3 days each.

Day 1:

Reintroduce one food group (ie dairy) you eliminated during the elimination phase. Eat it several times that day including various forms (ie milk, cheese, yogurt). Monitor for effects.

Day 2 & 3:

Take that food back out (go back to the full elimination diet) continuing to monitor for effects of the food you reintroduced.

At the end of Day 3, reassess for the possibility of moving on to the next reintroduction. If you are still experiencing negative symptoms from reintroducing the food, then stay on your elimination diet until your symptoms clear. Then you can proceed for the next reintroduction 3-day cycle.

As you move through the reintroduction phase, you keep returning to your elimination diet except for the day 1's that you are reintroducing one food.

Tracking Reintroduction Results

As you move through the reintroduction phase, use this chart to keep track of your results.

Food	Reintro Date	Results

Date _____

Su Mo Tu We Th Fr Sa

☀ ☁ 🌧 ❄ _____

⏰ **Wake up**
Time _____ **Energy** 1 2 3 4 5
Mood _____

Day 1 of 3
Reintroducing today: _____

Time	Food	Sup's/ Meds	Activity	Mood	Symptoms & Energy

Additional Abbreviations Used

My water intake ⊔ ⊔ ⊔ ⊔ ⊔ ⊔ ⊔ ⊔

Time	Food	Sup's/ Meds	Activity	Mood	Symptoms & Energy

Notes _____
_____
_____
_____
_____
_____

Time went to bed _____
Sleep quality _____
_____

Zzzzz...

Date _____

Wake up

Time _____ **Energy** 1 2 3 4 5

Mood _____

Day 2 of 3
Monitoring day

Time	Food	Sup's/ Meds	Activity	Mood	Symptoms & Energy

Additional Abbreviations Used

My water intake 🥛 🥛 🥛 🥛 🥛 🥛 🥛 🥛

Time	Food	Sup's/ Meds	Activity	Mood	Symptoms & Energy

Notes _____
_____
_____
_____
_____
_____

Time went to bed _____
Sleep quality _____

Zzzzz....

Day **3** Reintroduction Phase

Date _____

Su Mo Tu We Th Fr Sa

🕐 Wake up
Time _____ **Energy** 1 2 3 4 5
Mood _____

Day 3 of 3
Monitoring day

Time	Food	Sup's/ Meds	Activity	Mood	Symptoms & Energy

Additional Abbreviations Used					

My water intake

Time	Food	Sup's/ Meds	Activity	Mood	Symptoms & Energy

Notes _____
_____
_____
_____
_____

Time went to bed _____
Sleep quality _____
_____
_____

Date _____

Su Mo Tu We Th Fr Sa

⏰ **Wake up**
Time _____ **Energy** 1 2 3 4 5
Mood _____

Day 1 of 3
Reintroducing today: _____

Time	Food	Sup's/ Meds	Activity	Mood	Symptoms & Energy

Additional Abbreviations Used

My water intake

Time	Food	Sup's/ Meds	Activity	Mood	Symptoms & Energy

Notes _____
_____
_____
_____
_____
_____

Time went to bed _____
Sleep quality _____
_____
_____

Zzzzz...

Date _____

Su Mo Tu We Th Fr Sa

Wake up

Time _____ **Energy** 1 2 3 4 5

Mood _____

Day 2 of 3
Monitoring day

Time	Food	Sup's/ Meds	Activity	Mood	Symptoms & Energy

Additional Abbreviations Used					

My water intake   ⊔ ⊔ ⊔ ⊔ ⊔ ⊔ ⊔ ⊔

Time	Food	Sup's/ Meds	Activity	Mood	Symptoms & Energy

Notes _____
_____
_____
_____
_____
_____

Time went to bed _____
Sleep quality _____
_____
_____

Zzzz...

Day 6 Reintroduction Phase

Date _____

Su Mo Tu We Th Fr Sa

Wake up
Time _____ Energy 1 2 3 4 5
Mood _____

Day 3 of 3
Monitoring day

Time	Food	Sup's/ Meds	Activity	Mood	Symptoms & Energy

Additional Abbreviations Used

My water intake

Time	Food	Sup's/ Meds	Activity	Mood	Symptoms & Energy

Notes _____

_____

_____

_____

_____

Time went to bed _____
Sleep quality _____

_____

Zzzzz...

Day 7

Reintroduction Phase

Date _____

Su Mo Tu We Th Fr Sa

Wake up
Time _____ **Energy** 1 2 3 4 5
Mood _____

Day 1 of 3
Reintroducing today: _____

Time	Food	Sup's/ Meds	Activity	Mood	Symptoms & Energy

Additional Abbreviations Used

126

My water intake

Time	Food	Sup's/ Meds	Activity	Mood	Symptoms & Energy

Notes _____
_____
_____
_____
_____
_____

Time went to bed _____
Sleep quality _____
_____
_____

Zzzzz...

Day	8	Reintroduction Phase

Date _____

Su Mo Tu We Th Fr Sa

Wake up
Time _____ **Energy** 1 2 3 4 5
Mood _____

Day 2 of 3
Monitoring day

Time	Food	Sup's/ Meds	Activity	Mood	Symptoms & Energy

Additional Abbreviations Used

My water intake   🥛 🥛 🥛 🥛 🥛 🥛 🥛 🥛

Time	Food	Sup's/ Meds	Activity	Mood	Symptoms & Energy

Notes _____

_____

_____

_____

_____

Time went to bed _____
Sleep quality _____

_____

_____

Zzzz...

Day **9** Reintroduction Phase

Date _____

🕐 Wake up
Time _____ **Energy** 1 2 3 4 5
Mood _____

Day 3 of 3
Monitoring day

Time	Food	Sup's/ Meds	Activity	Mood	Symptoms & Energy

Additional Abbreviations Used

My water intake ⊔ ⊔ ⊔ ⊔ ⊔ ⊔ ⊔ ⊔

Time	Food	Sup's/ Meds	Activity	Mood	Symptoms & Energy

Notes _____
_____
_____
_____
_____
_____

Time went to bed _____
Sleep quality _____
_____
_____

131

Date _____

Su Mo Tu We Th Fr Sa

Wake up

Time _____ **Energy** 1 2 3 4 5

Mood _____

Day 1 of 3

Reintroducing today: _____

Time	Food	Sup's/ Meds	Activity	Mood	Symptoms & Energy

Additional Abbreviations Used

My water intake ▯ ▯ ▯ ▯ ▯ ▯ ▯ ▯

Time	Food	Sup's/ Meds	Activity	Mood	Symptoms & Energy

Notes _____

_____

_____

_____

_____

_____

Time went to bed _____
Sleep quality _____

_____

Zzzzz...

133

Date _____

Wake up
Time _____ Energy 1 2 3 4 5
Mood _____

Day 2 of 3
Monitoring day

Time	Food	Sup's/ Meds	Activity	Mood	Symptoms & Energy

Additional Abbreviations Used

My water intake

Time	Food	Sup's/ Meds	Activity	Mood	Symptoms & Energy

Notes _____

_____

_____

_____

_____

_____

Time went to bed _____

Sleep quality _____

_____

_____

Day 12 Reintroduction Phase		

Day **12** Reintroduction Phase

Date _____

Su Mo Tu We Th Fr Sa

Wake up
Time _____ **Energy** 1 2 3 4 5
Mood _____

Day 3 of 3
Monitoring day

Time	Food	Sup's/ Meds	Activity	Mood	Symptoms & Energy

Additional Abbreviations Used

My water intake

Time	Food	Sup's/ Meds	Activity	Mood	Symptoms & Energy

Notes _____

_____

_____

_____

_____

Time went to bed _____

Sleep quality _____

_____

Day 13 Reintroduction Phase

Wake up
Time _____ **Energy** 1 2 3 4 5
Mood _____

Day 1 of 3

Reintroducing today: _____

Time	Food	Sup's/ Meds	Activity	Mood	Symptoms & Energy

Additional Abbreviations Used

My water intake   🥛 🥛 🥛 🥛 🥛 🥛 🥛 🥛

Time	Food	Sup's/ Meds	Activity	Mood	Symptoms & Energy

Notes _____

_____

_____

_____

_____

_____

Time went to bed _____
Sleep quality _____

_____

_____

Date _____

Wake up
Time _____ **Energy** 1 2 3 4 5
Mood _____

Day 2 of 3
Monitoring day

Time	Food	Sup's/ Meds	Activity	Mood	Symptoms & Energy

Additional Abbreviations Used

My water intake 🥛 🥛 🥛 🥛 🥛 🥛 🥛 🥛

Time	Food	Sup's/ Meds	Activity	Mood	Symptoms & Energy

Notes _____

_____

_____

_____

_____

Time went to bed _____
Sleep quality _____

_____

_____

Date _____

Su Mo Tu We Th Fr Sa

Wake up
Time _____ Energy 1 2 3 4 5
Mood _____

Day 3 of 3
Monitoring day

Time	Food	Sup's/ Meds	Activity	Mood	Symptoms & Energy

Additional Abbreviations Used

My water intake ▯ ▯ ▯ ▯ ▯ ▯ ▯ ▯

Time	Food	Sup's/ Meds	Activity	Mood	Symptoms & Energy

Notes _____

_____

_____

_____

_____

Time went to bed _____
Sleep quality _____

_____

_____

Zzzzz...

Day 16 Reintroduction Phase

Date _____

Su Mo Tu We Th Fr Sa

Wake up
Time _____ **Energy** 1 2 3 4 5
Mood _____

Day 1 of 3

Reintroducing today: _____

Time	Food	Sup's/ Meds	Activity	Mood	Symptoms & Energy

Additional Abbreviations Used

My water intake

Time	Food	Sup's/Meds	Activity	Mood	Symptoms & Energy

Notes _____

_____

_____

_____

_____

Time went to bed _____
Sleep quality _____

_____

_____

Day 17 Reintroduction Phase

Su Mo Tu We Th Fr Sa

Wake up
Time _____ **Energy** 1 2 3 4 5
Mood _____

Day 2 of 3
Monitoring day

Time	Food	Sup's/ Meds	Activity	Mood	Symptoms & Energy

Additional Abbreviations Used

My water intake

Time	Food	Sup's/ Meds	Activity	Mood	Symptoms & Energy

Notes _____
_____
_____
_____
_____
_____

Time went to bed _____
Sleep quality _____

Zzzzz...

_____
_____

Day 18 Reintroduction Phase

Date _____

Su Mo Tu We Th Fr Sa

Wake up
Time _____ **Energy** 1 2 3 4 5
Mood _____

Day 3 of 3
Monitoring day

Time	Food	Sup's/ Meds	Activity	Mood	Symptoms & Energy

Additional Abbreviations Used

My water intake

Time	Food	Sup's/ Meds	Activity	Mood	Symptoms & Energy

Notes _____
_____
_____
_____
_____
_____

Time went to bed _____
Sleep quality _____
_____
_____

Zzzzz...

Day 19 Reintroduction Phase

Wake up
Time _____ Energy 1 2 3 4 5
Mood _____

Day 1 of 3

Reintroducing today: _____

Time	Food	Sup's/ Meds	Activity	Mood	Symptoms & Energy

Additional Abbreviations Used

My water intake ▯ ▯ ▯ ▯ ▯ ▯ ▯ ▯

Time	Food	Sup's/ Meds	Activity	Mood	Symptoms & Energy

Notes _____

_____

_____

_____

_____

_____

Time went to bed _____
Sleep quality _____

Zzzzz...

_____

_____

Date _____

 _____

 Wake up

Time _____ **Energy** 1 2 3 4 5

Mood _____

Day 2 of 3
Monitoring day

Time	Food	Sup's/ Meds	Activity	Mood	Symptoms & Energy

Additional Abbreviations Used					

My water intake

Time	Food	Sup's/ Meds	Activity	Mood	Symptoms & Energy

Notes _____

_____

_____

_____

_____

Time went to bed _____
Sleep quality _____

_____

_____

Day 21 Reintroduction Phase

Date _____

☀ ☁ 🌧 ❄ _____

Wake up
Time _____ **Energy** 1 2 3 4 5
Mood _____

Day 3 of 3
Monitoring day

Time	Food	Sup's/ Meds	Activity	Mood	Symptoms & Energy

Additional Abbreviations Used

My water intake ▢ ▢ ▢ ▢ ▢ ▢ ▢ ▢

Time	Food	Sup's/ Meds	Activity	Mood	Symptoms & Energy

Notes _____
_____
_____
_____
_____
_____

Time went to bed _____
Sleep quality _____
_____
_____

155

Day 22 Reintroduction Phase

Su Mo Tu We Th Fr Sa

_____

Wake up

Time _____ **Energy** 1 2 3 4 5

Mood _____

Day 1 of 3

Reintroducing today: _____

Time	Food	Sup's/ Meds	Activity	Mood	Symptoms & Energy

Additional Abbreviations Used

My water intake

Time	Food	Sup's/ Meds	Activity	Mood	Symptoms & Energy

Notes _____
_____
_____
_____
_____
_____

Time went to bed _____
Sleep quality _____
_____
_____

157

Date _____

Su Mo Tu We Th Fr Sa

Wake up
Time _____ Energy 1 2 3 4 5
Mood _____

Day 2 of 3
Monitoring day

Time	Food	Sup's/ Meds	Activity	Mood	Symptoms & Energy

Additional Abbreviations Used

My water intake

Time	Food	Sup's/ Meds	Activity	Mood	Symptoms & Energy

Notes _____
_____
_____
_____
_____
_____

Time went to bed _____
Sleep quality _____
_____
_____

Date _____

Su Mo Tu We Th Fr Sa

 _____

 Wake up
Time _____ **Energy** 1 2 3 4 5
Mood _____

Day 3 of 3
Monitoring day

Time	Food	Sup's/Meds	Activity	Mood	Symptoms & Energy

Additional Abbreviations Used

My water intake ⬜ ⬜ ⬜ ⬜ ⬜ ⬜ ⬜ ⬜

Time	Food	Sup's/ Meds	Activity	Mood	Symptoms & Energy

Notes _____

_____

_____

_____

_____

Time went to bed _____
Sleep quality _____

_____

_____

Zzzzz...

Day 25 Reintroduction Phase

Date _____

Su Mo Tu We Th Fr Sa

Wake up
Time _____ **Energy** 1 2 3 4 5
Mood _____

Day 1 of 3

Reintroducing today: _____

Time	Food	Sup's/ Meds	Activity	Mood	Symptoms & Energy

Additional Abbreviations Used

My water intake ☐ ☐ ☐ ☐ ☐ ☐ ☐ ☐

Time	Food	Sup's/ Meds	Activity	Mood	Symptoms & Energy

Notes _____

_____

_____

_____

_____

_____

Time went to bed _____
Sleep quality _____

_____

_____

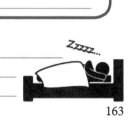

163

Date _____

_____

Wake up
Time _____ **Energy** 1 2 3 4 5
Mood _____

Day 2 of 3
Monitoring day

Time	Food	Sup's/ Meds	Activity	Mood	Symptoms & Energy

Additional Abbreviations Used

My water intake   ⊔ ⊔ ⊔ ⊔ ⊔ ⊔ ⊔ ⊔

Time	Food	Sup's/ Meds	Activity	Mood	Symptoms & Energy

Notes _____

_____

_____

_____

_____

_____

Time went to bed _____
Sleep quality _____

_____

_____

Zzzzz...

Date _____

Wake up
Time _____ Energy 1 2 3 4 5
Mood _____

Day 3 of 3
Monitoring day

Time	Food	Sup's/ Meds	Activity	Mood	Symptoms & Energy

Additional Abbreviations Used

My water intake ⬛ ⬛ ⬛ ⬛ ⬛ ⬛ ⬛ ⬛

Time	Food	Sup's/ Meds	Activity	Mood	Symptoms & Energy

Notes _____

_____

_____

_____

_____

_____

Time went to bed _____
Sleep quality _____

_____

Zzzzz...

Day 28 Reintroduction Phase

Date _____

Su Mo Tu We Th Fr Sa

_____

Wake up
Time _____ **Energy** 1 2 3 4 5
Mood _____

Day 1 of 3
Reintroducing today: _____

Time	Food	Sup's/ Meds	Activity	Mood	Symptoms & Energy

Additional Abbreviations Used

My water intake

Time	Food	Sup's/ Meds	Activity	Mood	Symptoms & Energy

Notes _____
_____
_____
_____
_____

Time went to bed _____
Sleep quality _____
_____
_____

Zzzzz...

Date _____

_____

Wake up
Time _____ **Energy** 1 2 3 4 5
Mood _____

Day 2 of 3
Monitoring day

Time	Food	Sup's/ Meds	Activity	Mood	Symptoms & Energy

Additional Abbreviations Used

My water intake ⊔ ⊔ ⊔ ⊔ ⊔ ⊔ ⊔ ⊔

Time	Food	Sup's/ Meds	Activity	Mood	Symptoms & Energy

Notes _____
_____
_____
_____
_____
_____

Time went to bed _____
Sleep quality _____
_____
_____

Zzzzz...

Date _____

_____

 **Wake up**
Time _____ **Energy** 1 2 3 4 5
Mood _____

Day 3 of 3
Monitoring day

Time	Food	Sup's/ Meds	Activity	Mood	Symptoms & Energy

Additional Abbreviations Used

My water intake ☐ ☐ ☐ ☐ ☐ ☐ ☐ ☐

Time	Food	Sup's/ Meds	Activity	Mood	Symptoms & Energy

Notes _____
_____
_____
_____
_____
_____

Time went to bed _____
Sleep quality _____
_____
_____

Zzzzz...

Reflections on Reintroduction Phase

Tracking Reintroduction Results

Foods that Passed Test	Foods that Failed Test

Reflections on Moving Forward

About the Author

Ann Silvers, MA
Counselor, Relationship Coach,
Hypnotherapist and Author

I haven't always been a counselor. During my first career, I was a Medical Lab Tech working in Microbiology labs in a couple of large hospitals in Canada.

When I experienced profound positive changes from psychotherapy as a client, I decided that I wanted to reroute my focus away from microorganisms onto helping people, so I returned to school to get all the degrees necessary to become a counselor.

I always asked my clients some questions about diet, exercise, and supplements, but that part of my practice has grown dramatically through training in the exciting new field of nutritional psychology.

Getting a Certificate in Integrative Medicine for Mental Health has brought together my background in science and medicine, life-long interest in nutrition, and work as a counselor.

You can find me on social media and annsilvers.com (my eStore and blog).

Made in United States
Troutdale, OR
12/11/2023

15682133R00106